EASY ARRANGEMENTS FOR PIANO SOLO

The Best-Known Blues Tunes

From 'The Classic Piano Course'

Arranged by BARRIE CARSON TURNER

Chester Music
(A division of Music Sales Limited)
8/9 Frith Street, London W1V 5TZ

Exclusive Distributors: Music Sales Limited,
Newmarket Road, Bury St Edmunds, Suffolk IP33 3YB

This book © Copyright 2000 Chester Music
Order No. CH61531. ISBN 0-7119-7692-9

Music processed by New Notations
Printed in the United Kingdom by Caligraving Limited, Thetford, Norfolk

Contents

Love Is Blue (L'Amour Est Bleu)

Original Words by Pierre Cour
English Lyrics by Bryan Blackburn
Music by André Popp

The Lonesome Road

Words by Gene Austin
Music by Nathaniel Shilkret

Moderately; rocking tempo

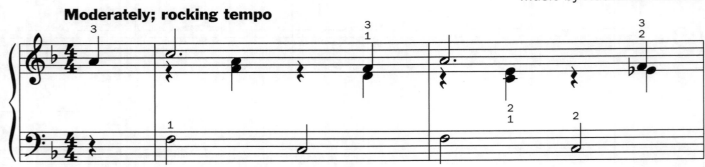

Solitude

Words by Eddie de Lange & Irving Mills
Music by Duke Ellington

Slowly, with expression

Georgia On My Mind

Words by Stuart Gorrell
Music by Hoagy Carmichael

Lover Man (Oh Where Can You Be)

Words & Music by Jimmy Davis,
Roger Ramirez & Jimmy Sherman

* Original ♩ ♩ ♩

Mood Indigo

Words & Music by Duke Ellington, Irving Mills & Albany Bigard

Blue And Sentimental

Words & Music by Count Basie, Jerry Livingston & Mack David

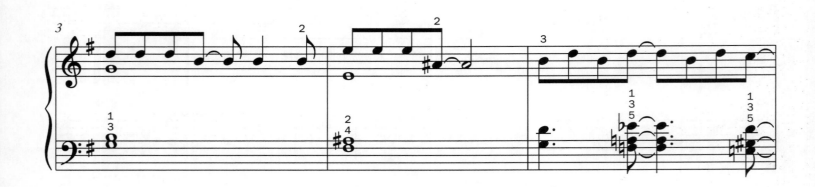

Round Midnight

Words by Bernard Hanighen
By Cootie Williams & Thelonious Monk

Moderately slow

To ⊕ Coda

* Original ♩ ♩ ♩

Angel Eyes

Words by Earl Brent
Music by Matt Dennis

Slow blues tempo

That Ole Devil Called Love

Words & Music by Doris Fisher & Allan Roberts

Medium slow blues tempo

Basin Street Blues

Words and music by Spencer Williams

Walkin' Blues

Words & Music by Robert Johnson

The Lady Sings The Blues

Words by Billie Holiday
Music by Herbie Nichols

Slow blues tempo

EASY PIANO REPERTOIRE

POP TUNES YOU'VE ALWAYS WANTED TO PLAY

Over 35 of the greatest pop songs spanning four decades. Arranged for easy piano solo.
CH61631

CHRISTMAS TUNES YOU'VE ALWAYS WANTED TO PLAY

Over 70 popular Christmas carols and songs, arranged for easy piano solo with words and chord symbols.
CH61632

SHOW TUNES YOU'VE ALWAYS WANTED TO PLAY

Over 130 pages of the best-loved songs from the shows. Arranged for easy piano solo.
CH61687

TUNES YOU'VE ALWAYS WANTED TO PLAY

FILM TUNES YOU'VE ALWAYS WANTED TO PLAY

Over 40 of the best known themes and songs from the greatest films.
CH61688

DUETS YOU'VE ALWAYS WANTED TO PLAY

Over 100 pages of all-time favourites, arranged for easy piano duet.
CH61185

TUNES YOU'VE ALWAYS WANTED TO PLAY

An outstanding album containing classical and traditional melodies.
CH55834

Available from Music Sales

Music Sales Limited, Sales & Distribution
Newmarket Road, Bury St Edmunds, Suffolk, IP33 3YB
Sales: 01284 705 050